CONTENTS

£6.99

STARS OF THE SHOW!

Discover all there is to know about your favourite looney tunes!

BUGS BUNNY

The unbeatable Bugs Bunny will take on any scheming rabbit hunter and tie them up in knots! Elmer Fudd is no match for this smart bunny who always manages to escape Elmer's traps.

LOONEY FACT:

Bugs Bunny's favourite catchphrase is "Ehh, what's up, doc?"

TAZ

Tasmanian Devil, or Taz for short, spins around like a tornado and is always hungry. This furry beast is always on a mission to find his next meal. Beware, because Taz will eat anything!

LOONEY FACT:

Taz has a soft spot for a female Tasmanian Devil called She Devil.

DAFFY DUCK

Daffy wants to be the best at everything but sadly, there's always someone better than him - and that makes him mad! He loves to pit his wits against Bugs but Daffy always comes off worst.

LOONEY FACT:

Daffy Duck loves to shout "You're desthpicable!"

Tweety and Sylvester

TWEETY AND SYLVESTER

Tweety is a cute little yellow canary whose feathers never get ruffled, even when he is in danger. The danger usually comes from Sylvester who is desperate to catch the little bird for his dinner!

LOONEY FACT:
Tweety and Sylvester live with Granny, a sweet old lady who is devoted to her pet canary.

ROAD RUNNER

Road Runner is a super-speedy toon who always manages to outrun his rival, Wile. E. Coyote. Wile sets up all sorts of traps to catch Road Runner but they never work and Wile usually ends up in a painful heap.

LOONEY FACT:
All of Wile's traps and devices come from the Acme Corporation.

NAME THAT TOON!

Can you match these Looney stars up with their names?

 ①  ②  ③  ④

A) MARVIN THE MARTIAN **C) PORKY PIG**
B) PEPE LE PEW **D) ELMER FUDD**

THE DUCK WITH NO NAME

WB 153

Writer: Jack Enyart Artist: George Wildman Letterer: Nick Napolitano Colorist: Duendes del Sur

SAN RODENTO SALUTES SPEEDY! SAVIOUR OF OUR TOWN FOR THE... ...... 456 TIME

AS MAYOR OF SAN RODENTO...

...AND AS JUDGE...

...AND SHERIFF, WE EXPRESS GRATITUDE TO OUR HERO, *SPEEDY GONZALES!*

SI, SI! SPEEDY!!

SI, SI! SPEEDY!!

CLAP

CLAP

CLAP

HOKEY, HOKAY. I SPEAK! BUT YOU MAY NOT LIKE WHAT I SAY...

SPEECH

SPEECH

SPEECH

CLAP

ONCE AGAIN AMIGOS, I HAVE SAVED YOU FROM THE DREADED BANDIT *SERAPE SAM.* I FEEL, THOUGH, THEES CANNOT GO ON!

TIP TIP TIP

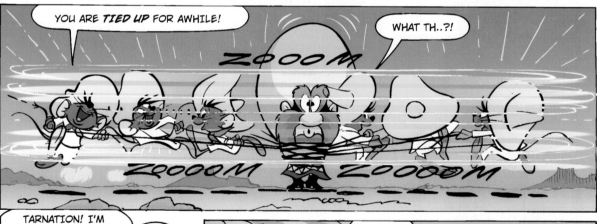

CLAP CLAP

BRAVO SPEEDY!

OUR HERO...

...AGAIN!

CARAMBA, NOW I HAVE TO CHANGE THE BANNER... *AGAIN!*

IT WEELL BE THE LAST TIME, COUSIN SLOWPOKE...

YOU CANNOT ALWAYS DEPEND ON OTHERS. FROM NOW ON I, SPEEDY GONZALES, WILL *NOT* HELP YOU!

WHAT...!

BUT...?

HOW...?!

YOU WEELL SEE. IT IS FOR YOUR OWN GOOD!

BUT, SPEEDY! WE ARE POOR FARMER MICE...

WE KNOW NOTHING OF FIGHTING!

WHAT IF SAM RETURNS? HE WILL STEAL OUR CROPS!

YOU MUST LEARN TO STAND UP FOR YOURSELVES. YOU WILL THANK ME ONE DAY!

FRUIT

FRUIT

LOOK! SMOKE SIGNALS! COULD THAT BE...?

JUST WAIT 'TIL THEM RATTY PEONS GET THIS MESSAGE...!

So, the mice of San Rodento sought a *new hero!*

WANTED
GUNFIGHTER

Hmm... this looks like a good deal...

It's been a long time since I've had good Tex-Mex!

PAY
ALL
YOU CAN EAT

It es hopeless....

How will we possibly find someone, before dawn?

You *have* amigos. Just call me...

...the duck with no name!

You need a gunfighter? Thats *me*...

WANTED

I'm purt' well-know, north of the border, many's the ornery hombre I've faced!

"Eat lead!"

"Eat lead!"

"I'm eating..."

I'm eating..."

....

Frankly, that's why I'm here. I'm *tired* of eating *lead!*

CONTINUED ON PAGE 12 ▶

LISTEN UP! AS MAYOR, JUDGE AND SHERIFF I HEREBY DECREE SOME CHANGES 'ROUND HERE...

NAMELY, *NEW LAWS!*

NO ONE APPROACHES ME 'CEPT ON THEIR KNEES! NO SMILIN' IN MY IMPERIAL PRESENCE! AND NO MOUSTACHES IN TOWN, 'CEPT MINE...!

NO *MOUSTACHES?!*

NO WAY, JOSE!

GET HIM!!

SI!!!!

SI!!!!

AHA! IT'S HAPPENING, JUST AS I PLANNED...

BOO!!

RUN HIM OUT OF TOWN!

WA-WAS IT SOMETHING *I SAID?*

FEATHERS

WAIT UP! DON'T FORGET THE *GUACAMOLE!*

TAR

YOU SEE? FACED WITH TYRANNY, THE TOWNSFOLK HAVE STOOD UP *FOR THEMSELVES!*

CARAMBA! WE HAVE LEARNED OUR LESSON WELL BUT, WHAT OF THE DUCK WITH NO NAME?

DON'T WORRY. *HE* GETS PAID, NO MATTER WHAT!

IS IT LEON, MAYBE? IRVING? I KNOW: CLINT! YOUR NAME IS *CLINT...!*

MUNCH, MUNCH. *SHADDUP!*

ADIOS, AMIGOS!

1 Cut the top flaps away from the cardboard box. Trim two of the sides diagonally so that they are sloping.

2 Draw the shape of Bugs Bunny's head onto card, cut it out, draw around it and cut it out again. Glue the shapes together for strength and glue it onto the back of the box.

3 Cut a piece of card that will slot into the middle of the box. Cut it along the top to look like wavy grass. Cover the whole thing with two layers of papier mache and leave to dry.

4 Roll up two pieces of thin card and use tape to secure them. Cover each of them with papier mache and fix inside the tidy as carrot pen holders.

5 Paint Bugs with grey, pink and white paint. Paint the carrots orange with black wavy lines on them. Paint the grass green and the box blue.

6 Once it's dry, cut out some leaves from felt and glue them to the top of the carrots!

DEMOLITION DEVIL

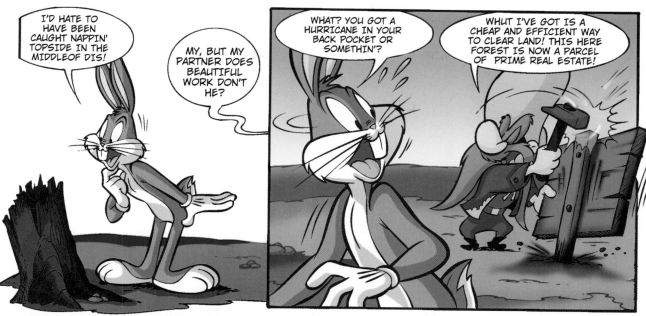

CONTINUED ON PAGE 30 ▸

THE BRAIN GAME!

Use your brain power to solve this game. Study the scene for one minute and then cover the page up.
Now it's time to answer the questions on the right!

Now cover the picture and thsee if you can get more questionsth right than brainy old me!

1 What is written on the tree?
A) I love Bugs
B) I love to read
C) Taz smells

2 What colour is Bugs' book?
A) Blue B) Pink
C) Purple

3 How many cakes are on the plate?
A) 1 B) 5 C) 2

4 True or false
Taz is eating an apple

5 What is Tweety doing?
A) Walking
B) Sitting
C) Flying

6 Which of these books is Sylvester reading?
A WATCHING BIRDS
B TOUCHY SUBJECT
C GOOD TASTE

7 True or false
There is an insect buzzing around Bugs Bunny's ears

8 How many daisies can you see?
A) 16 B) 14 C) 15

27

Happy Holidays!

The Looney Tunes are packing for their holidays! Can you fit the name of each item they need into the grid.

ACROSS

2 5 6 7

DOWN

1 2 3 4 6

29

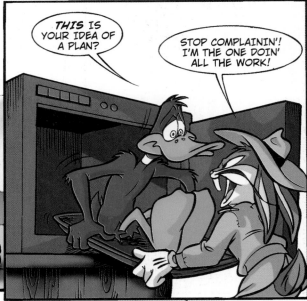

THAT'S ALL FOLKS!

1 Fill the sock with cotton wool as you work to make it easier to decorate. Glue a strip of white felt around the 'neck' of the sock.

2 Draw around the end of the sock onto paper. Draw around these lines to make the shape of Daffy's beak.

3 Use the paper template that you have made to cut two shapes from orange felt. Glue them together around the edge, leaving the straight edge unglued. This will be the beak.

4 Turn the beak inside out to hide the seams and glue it onto the end of the sock.

5 Glue on two white eyes and a scrap of black spiky hair!

6 Use the black fabric paint to add Daffy's pupils and nostrils and leave to dry.

VROOOOOAAR!

THAT'S ALL FOLKS!

WITCH GRAFT

EARL KRESS -- Writer
OMAR ARANDA -- Pencils
ALBERTO SAICHANN -- Inks
TOM ORZECHOWSKI -- Letterer
DAVE TANGUAY -- Colorist
HARVEY RICHARDS -- Asst. Editor
JOAN HILTY -- Editor

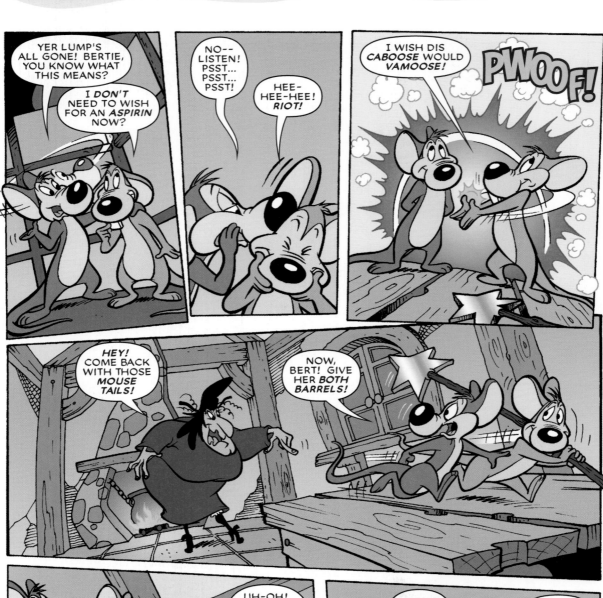

What's Cooking?

Taz, Porky Pig and Bugs Bunny are cooking for Tweety. Can you work out which chef has got everything on Tweety's list?

Tweety's Menu
Salsa
Pizza
Hamburger
Milkshake
Ice cream sundae
Cheese
Cake

Funny Bunny!

Can you help Bugs Bunny to find all of the words hidden in the grid?

I	D	S	H	N	E	T	I	M	A	N	Y	D
M	O	K	I	R	K	M	O	B	B	S	B	O
P	E	L	A	A	C	M	E	L	A	Z	A	C
O	W	E	C	B	U	R	R	O	W	U	Y	D
R	B	C	I	B	D	R	T	L	I	V	N	A
K	E	U	Q	I	Y	P	Z	A	A	J	C	R
Y	S	T	Y	T	F	L	S	B	H	E	Y	H
P	T	T	U	T	F	A	T	U	K	T	D	A
I	T	E	L	L	A	M	A	N	R	C	A	R
G	E	L	E	S	D	Z	C	N	W	A	D	E
P	A	D	U	W	A	U	T	Y	A	E	C	K
C	A	R	R	O	T	J	X	R	E	M	L	E

DAFFY DUCK **TAZ** DOC
LETTUCE
RABBIT DYNAMITE
CARROT MALLET PORKY PIG
RACE BURROW ACME
LOLA BUNNY ANVIL
ELMER HARE

Who is the owner of this pair of feet? Find their name hidden in the grid.

51

Fee, Fi, Fo, FUDD

BILL MATHENY-WRITER
DAVID ALVAREZ-PENCILLER
MIKE DECARLO-INKER • NICK J. NAP-LETTERER
DAVE TANGUAY-COLORIST
HARVEY RICHARDS-ASST EDITOR
JOAN HILTY-EDITOR

LOONEY TUNES 112. May, 2004. Published monthly by DC Comics, 1700 Broadway, New York, NY 10019. POSTMASTER: Send address changes to LOONEY TUNES, DC Comics Subscriptions, P.O. Box 0528, Baldwin, NY 11510. Annual subscription rate (12 issues) $27.00. Canadian subscribers must add $12.00 for postage and GST. GST # is R125921072. All foreign countries must add $12.00 for postage. U.S. funds only. The stories, characters and incidents mentioned in this magazine are entirely fictional. Printed on recyclable paper. DC Comics does not read or accept unsolicited submissions of ideas, stories or artwork.
Printed in Canada.

DC Comics, a Warner Bros. Entertainment Company

• DAN DIDIO, VP-Editorial • PAUL LEVITZ, President & Publisher • GEORG BREWER, VP-Design & Retail Product Development •
• RICHARD BRUNING, Sr. VP-Creative Director • PATRICK CALDON, Senior VP-Finance & Operations • CHRIS CARAMALIS, VP-Finance • TERRI CUNNINGHAM, VP-Managing Editor •
• ALISON GILL, VP-Manufacturing • LILLIAN LASERSON, Sr. VP & General Counsel • JIM LEE, Editorial Director-Wildstorm •
• DAVID McKILLIPS, VP-Advertising & Custom Publishing • JOHN NEE, VP-Business Development •
• CHERYL RUBIN, VP-Brand Management • BOB WAYNE, VP-Sales & Marketing •

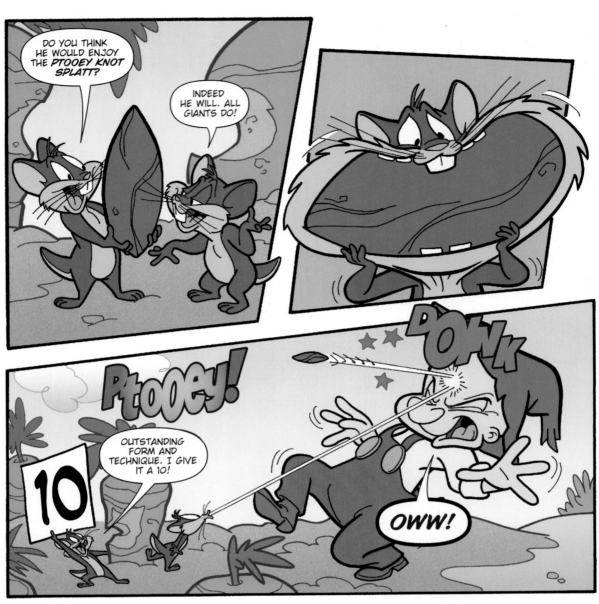

CONTINUED ON PAGE 58 ▶

1 Draw a large Taz shape onto card and cut it out. Draw around it and cut it out again, gluing the two shapes together for strength.

2 Cut a strip of card. Tape it into a hoop shape. Cover the Taz shape and the hoop with 2-3 layers of papier maché and leave to dry.

3 Paint Taz with two shades of brown paint, and add details with black and white paint. Paint the hoop with bright green paint.

4 Tie lots of lengths of wool into pairs, and use sticky tape to fix them inside the hoop, about 2cm apart.

5 Take one strand from one pair and one strand from the next pair and tie them into a knot. Take the remaining strand from one of these pairs and tie it to one from the next pair. Repeat all the way around the hoop to form the net. Keep going as long as you like. Taz went round the hoop five times.

6 Glue the hoop onto Tax, then fix it to your wall for some basketball practice!

ANSWERS!

Page 5: Stars of the Show
1-C, 2-D, 3-A, 4-B

Page 11: Lost in Space
B

Page 17: Get the Message
Dear Pets please tidy the house and make the tea

Page 26-27: The Brain Game
1-B, 2-A, 3-C, 4-False 5-C, 6-A,
7-True, 8-B

Page 28: Look Again

Page 29:
Happy Holiday

Page 44: Duck and Dive
1-B, 2-A, 3-F, 4-D, 5-C, 6 doesn't have an identical twin, 7-H, 8-E, 9-G

Page 45: Ready Set Go

START

Page 50: What's Cooking
Porky has everything on Tweety's list

Page 51: Funny Buuny

```
I D S H N E T I M A N Y D
M O K I R K M O B B S B O
P E L A A C M E L A Z A C
O W E C B U R R O W U Y D
R B C I B D R T L I V N A
K E U Q I Y P Z A A J C R
Y S T Y T F L S B H E Y H
P T T U T F A T U K T D A
I T E L L A M A N R C A R
G E L E S D Z C N W A D E
P A D U W A U T Y A E C K
C A R R O T J X R E M L E
```

Tweety is the hidden name